Picture Kelpies

Picture Kelpies is an imprint of Floris Books
First published in 2010 by Floris Books Third printing 2012

www.florisbooks.co.uk
The publisher acknowledges subsidy from Creative Scotland
towards the publication of this volume.
British Library CIP Data available
ISBN 978-086315-746-2
Printed in China

For a whole week, Gregor MacDonald had been really good. His dad had promised him a special birthday present if he helped around the house.

Finally, the big day arrived. There on his father's desk was a large wooden box. "Bagpipes!" Gregor grinned. "Now I can be just like Grandad!"

Lifting the pipes, Gregor took a deep breath and blew as hard as he could.

HONK-EeYYoW!

"STOP!" yelled Dad, his fingers in his ears. "I think you need to practise. But one thing's for sure ... YOU CAN'T PLAY HERE!"

I ♥ DAD

After school, Gregor raced home and dashed up to his bedroom to practise his pipes. His wee dog Bert was waiting on the stairs.

Gregor stood in the middle of his room, took a deep breath and blew as hard as he could.

A few moments later, a loud tapping noise came from the kitchen below.

Rushing downstairs, he found his mum standing on a chair with a broom in her hands, banging on the ceiling.

"Gregor!" she said. "What a racket! You'll have to go outside … YOU CAN'T PLAY HERE!"

On Saturday, Gregor put his pipes in his backpack and went off with Bert to find a place to practise.

He soon came to a small loch. "This looks like a good spot," he said to himself.

He lifted his pipes, took a deep breath and blew as hard as he could.

All seemed well until Gregor noticed a rowing boat with three men, who were all cheering and waving at him.

But as the boat came closer Gregor could see that they weren't cheering … and they weren't waving. In fact, they didn't look thrilled at all.

"Stop that noise!"

"You're scaring the fish."

"YOU CAN'T PLAY HERE!" they shouted.

Gregor shoved his pipes back into the pack and trudged wearily away, towards the MacDougall's farm.

A small stone building stood in the corner of a field. It seemed to be empty.

"Great!" Gregor exclaimed. "I won't disturb anybody here."

He whisked out the bagpipes, took a deep breath and blew as hard as he could.

Suddenly, the air filled with swirling white feathers as ten startled pigeons all tried to get out of the building at the same time.

"Oh no!" moaned Gregor. "Mr MacDougall's racing pigeons!"

He peeped outside and saw a big, fat man with a bright red face brandishing a large, knobbly stick as he struggled across the field. All Gregor heard was:

"STOP! ... Pigeons ... YOU CAN'T PLAY HERE!" He didn't wait to hear more.

"Now where can I practise?" gasped Gregor as he and Bert sprinted across the fields.

"I know!" Gregor thought. "I can't disturb anybody in the middle of a field."

So, as Bert chased rabbits, Gregor lifted up his pipes, took a deep breath and blew as hard as he could.

A short while later, he stopped. "That's strange," he muttered. "The ground seems to be bouncing …"

A cloud of dust was moving quickly towards him … and some sharp horns … and beady black eyes.

"RUN, BERT! IT'S A BULL! WE CAN'T PLAY HERE!"

They only just escaped by leaping over the fence. They stumbled into a small clearing in the woods.

"This place will do nicely," Gregor thought. He took a deep breath and blew as hard as he could.

Two hunters covered in twigs and leaves bustled out of the trees, carrying long guns. They weren't happy.

"You there!" shouted one of the men. "You've scared off the stag we've been stalking all morning. YOU CAN'T PLAY HERE!"

But Gregor had already disappeared. Trudging along a steep path, he gazed around and realised he was now high in the hills.

"Of course, the mountains!" he shouted happily. "The perfect place for playing the bagpipes."

He picked up his pipes, took a deep breath and blew as hard as he could.

He had only been playing for a few minutes when he heard a funny squeaky-squawky noise.

Thinking that the pipes were out of tune, Gregor stopped … but the squeaking and squawking didn't! He looked up.

On a ledge above him, two large brown birds with hooked yellow beaks and razor-sharp claws stared down at him. They were golden eagles … and they didn't look pleased. Gregor was terrified and began putting away his pipes.

"Oi! You there!"

A man appeared with a bobble hat on his head and a pair of binoculars around his neck. He was shaking his fist.

"You're disturbing the birds … YOU CAN'T PLAY HERE!"

Gregor opened his mouth to say sorry, when suddenly …

Whoosh!

the eagles swooped. Gregor grabbed a shivering Bert, stuffed him under his arm and sprinted away.

He was utterly fed up. He only wanted to practise his new bagpipes but it seemed as if the whole world was against him.

Gregor didn't notice that he had stumbled into a lovely, well-kept garden. He slumped on to a wooden bench and put his head in his hands.

"Where, oh where, can I practise my pipes?" he cried.

"What about here?" asked a kind lady standing in front of him. Gregor thought she looked familiar, but was too excited to worry about it for long.

The next day, he made his way eagerly to the lady's grand house where a man in a smart uniform gave him a sharp salute and ushered him into the grounds.

Gregor found a good spot beneath some tall Scots pine trees and, taking a deep breath, he blew as hard as he could.

He played … and he played … and he played. From then on, Gregor visited the house every day and practised in the garden without bothering anyone, or anything.

When he stopped for a rest, the lady waved him over and a nice man brought him lemonade and biscuits on a silver tray. Gregor couldn’t have been happier.

A few months later, Gregor was having breakfast when there was a loud knock at the door. His dad answered it and returned, looking puzzled, with a fancy card in his hand.

"What's going on?" he asked.

Gregor started to explain about the nice lady's garden.

"Gregor!" his dad interrupted in a serious voice. "Do you know who that lady is?" He dropped the fancy card on the kitchen table.

Gregor read the exquisite gold lettering and realised immediately why the lady had looked familiar:

Her Majesty Queen Elizabeth II
Requests the pleasure of her friend
Gregor MacDonald
to lead Her Majesty's special birthday procession
of 100 pipers along Princes Street, Edinburgh

R.S.V.P

His dad smiled and ruffled Gregor's hair. "It looks like we have a real piper in the family again. Your grandad would have been so proud. You'd better do some practice then, and from now on, you *can* play here!"

This book is dedicated to the author's grandad Bob,
who inspired him to play the pipes.